· ONE MORE TIME 6 ·

Sing a Song of Christmas
Revised

· CONTENTS ·

Arranged by Stephen Clark
Cover Photo Barry Moore

First Published 1992

© International Music Publications
Southend Road, Woodford Green,
Essex IG8 8HN, England.

215-2-764

7-95

Medley 1

HAVE YOURSELF A MERRY LITTLE CHRISTMAS

Words and Music by HUGH MARTIN and RALPH BLANE

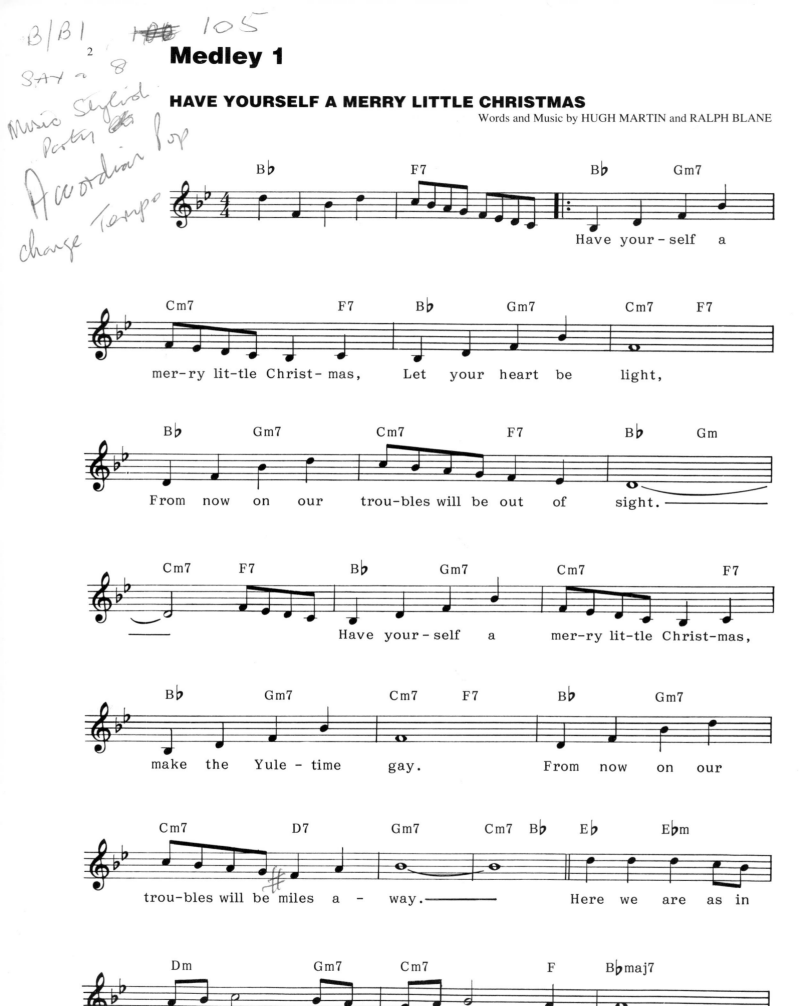

ROCKIN' AROUND THE CHRISTMAS TREE

Words and Music by JOHNNY MARKS

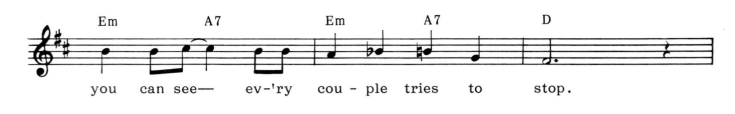

you can see— ev-'ry cou - ple tries to stop.

Rock-in' a - round the Christ - mas tree— let the

Christ-mas spi - rit ring.—— La-ter we'll have some

pump-kin pie— and we'll do some car - ol - ing.

You will get a sen - ti - ment-al feel-ing when you

hear Voi - ces sing - ing, "Let's be jol - ly,

Deck the hall with boughs of hol - ly." Rock-in' a - round the

Christ-mas tree— Have a hap - py hol - i - day.——

Ev-'ry-one danc-ing mer-ri-ly— in the new old fash-ioned way.

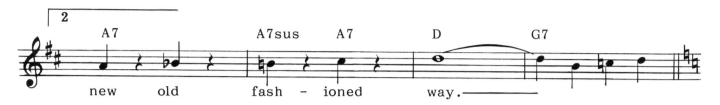

new old fash - ioned way.———

Sax or Read +8   130
(27 +8)

JINGLE-BELL ROCK

Words and Music by JOE BEAL and JIM BOOTHE

Jin-gle - bell, jin - gle - bell, jin - gle - bell rock.—

Jin-gle-bell swing and jin-gle-bell ring. Snow-in' and blow-in' up

bush-els of fun, Now the jin-gle hop has be-gun.—

Jin-gle-bell, jin-gle-bell, jin-gle-bell rock.— Jin-gle-bells chime in

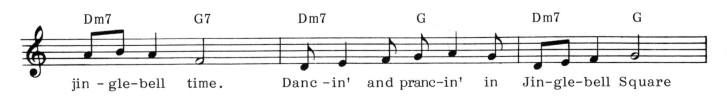

jin-gle-bell time. Danc-in' and pranc-in' in Jin-gle-bell Square

SNOWY WHITE SNOW AND JINGLE BELLS

Words and Music by JOHNNY SHERIDAN, RALPH RUVIN,
HAROLD IRVING, DENNIS BERGER and BILLY REID

Medley 2

CHRISTIANS AWAKE

Traditional

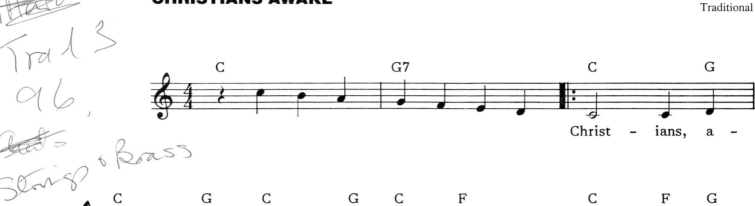

Christ - ians, a -

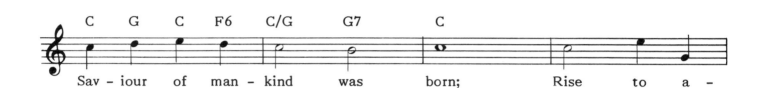

- wake, sa - lute the hap - py morn Where - on the

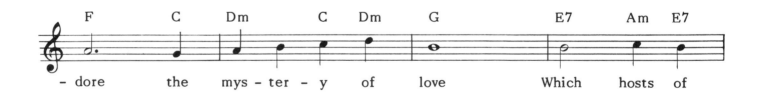

Sav - iour of man - kind was born; Rise to a -

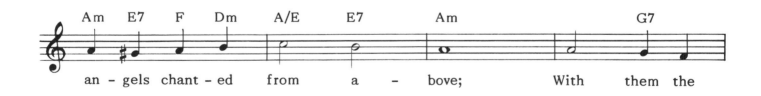

- dore the mys - ter - y of love Which hosts of

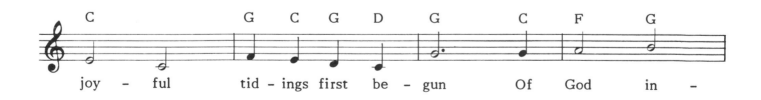

an - gels chant - ed from a - bove; With them the

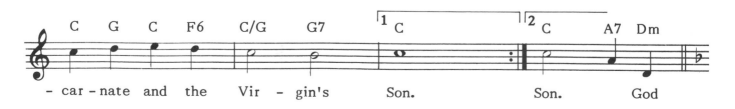

joy - ful tid - ings first be - gun Of God in -

- car - nate and the Vir - gin's Son. Son. God

GOD REST YOU MERRY, GENTLEMEN

© 1992 International Music Publications Southend Road, Woodford Green, Essex IG8 8HN

UNTO US A BOY IS BORN

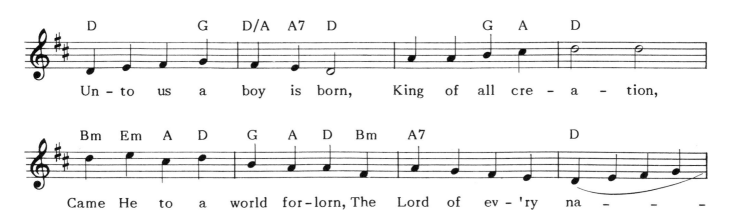

© 1992 International Music Publications Southend Road, Woodford Green, Essex IG8 8HN

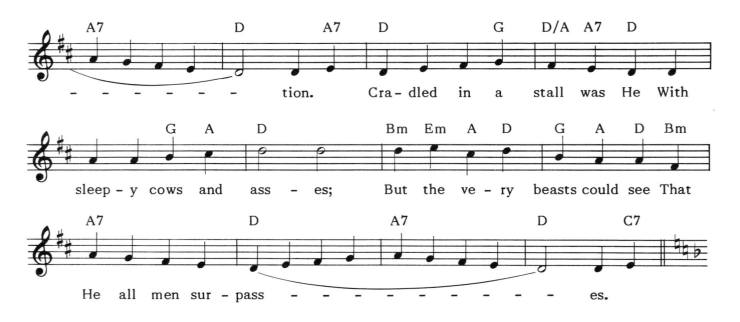

A7　　D　　A7　　D　　G　D/A　A7　D

– – – – – – tion. Cra – dled in a stall was He With

G　A　D　Bm　Em　A　D　G　A　D　Bm

sleep – y cows and ass – es; But the ve – ry beasts could see That

A7　　D　　A7　　D　　C7

He all men sur – pass – – – – – – es.

GOOD KING WENCESLAS

Traditional

F　　C7　F　Bb　C　　Bb　F　Bb　C

Good King Wen – ces – las looked out, On the feast of

F　　C7　F　Bb　C

Ste – phen, When the snow lay round a – bout,

Bb　F　Bb　C　F　　C7　　F　A7　Dm

Deep and crisp and e – ven; Bright – ly shone the moon that night,

Bb　F　Bb　C7　F　　Bb　A7　Dm　C

Though the frost was cru – el, When a poor man came in sight

F　Bb　F/C　C7　|1 Dm　Bb　F　C7　|2 F　Bb　F　Bb

Gath – 'ring win – ter fu – el.

F　Bb　F　C#°　Dm　Bbm　F

Gath – 'ring win – ter fu – el. ———

Medley 3

IN DULCI JUBILO

Traditional

In dul – ci ju – bi –

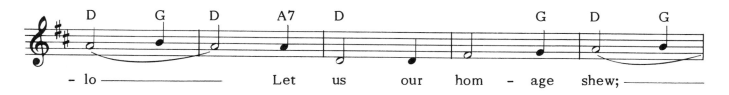

– lo ———— Let us our hom – age shew; ————

—— Our heart's joy re – clin – eth In proe –

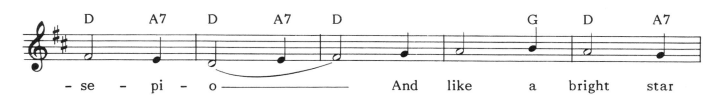

– se – pi – o ———— And like a bright star

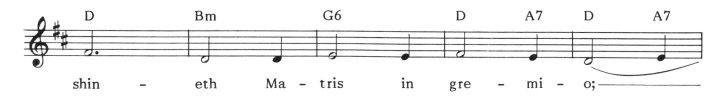

shin – eth Ma – tris in gre – mi – o; ————

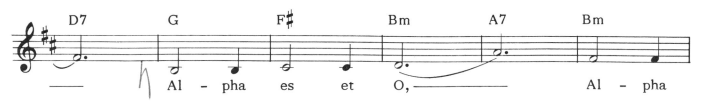

———— Al – pha es et O, ———— Al – pha

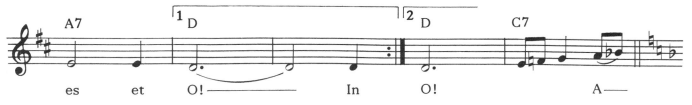

es et O! ———— In O! A——

A VIRGIN MOST PURE

Traditional

Vir - gin most — pure, — as the pro - phets do tell, Hath — brought forth a — Ba - by, as — it — hath be - fel, To — be our Re - deem - er from death, hell — and sin, Which — A - dam's trans - gres - sion hath — wrap - ped us in. And — there - fore be mer - ry, set sor - row — a - side; Christ — Je - sus our — Sav - iour was — born — on this tide. A — tide. Was -

WASSAIL, WASSAIL, ALL OVER THE TOWN!

Traditional

- sail, Was - sail, — all o - ver the town! — Our toast it is white, and our ale — it — is brown, Our

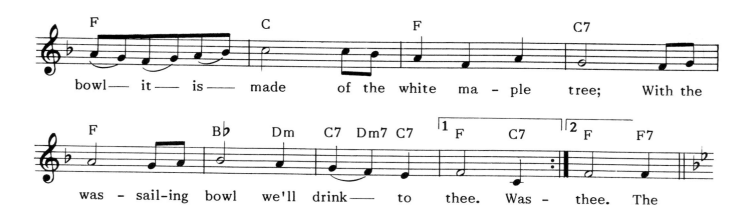

bowl — it — is — made of the white ma - ple tree; With the

was - sail-ing bowl we'll drink — to thee. Was - thee. The

MISTLETOE AND WINE

Words by LESLIE STEWART and JEREMY PAUL
Music by KEITH STRACHAN

child is a — king, the car - ol - lers — sing, The old is

passed, there's a new — be - gin - ning. Dreams of San - ta,

dreams of snow, Fin - gers numb, fa - ces a - glow. It's

Christ - mas time, mistletoe and wine, Child - ren sing - ing

Christ - i - an rhyme With logs on the fire — and gifts on the tree; A

time to re - joice in the good that we see. The see.

Medley 4

ALL I WANT FOR CHRISTMAS IS MY TWO FRONT TEETH

Words and Music by DON GARDNER

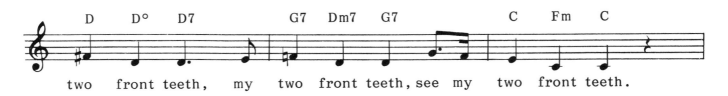

All I want for Christ-mas is my

two front teeth, my two front teeth, see my two front teeth.

Gee, if I could on - ly have my two front teeth, then

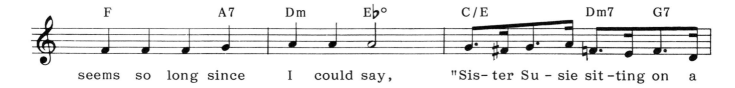

I could wish you "Mer - ry Christ - mas." It

seems so long since I could say, "Sis - ter Su - sie sit -ting on a

this - tle."— Gosh, oh gee, how hap-py I'd be, if

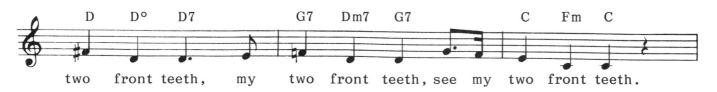

I could on - ly whis-tle (thhh!) All I want for Christ-mas is my

two front teeth, my two front teeth, see my two front teeth.

Gee, if I could on - ly have my two front teeth, then I could wish you "Mer - ry Christ-mas." Christ-mas." Christ-mas."

THE FAIRY ON THE CHRISTMAS TREE

Words by ROMA CAMPBELL HUNTER
Music by HARRY PARR-DAVIES

Ev-'ry lit- tle girl would like to be the fair - y on the Christ-mas tree, Up a-bove the par - ty, dressed in white, shin - ing in the can - dle light. Ev- 'ry lit- tle boy has lots of fun with his trum - pet and his gun. Ev- 'ry lit-tle girl you un-der-stand is real-ly queen of fair- y -land.

Black gol-ly-wogs; wee wool-ly dogs; big beau-ti-ful bears.

Most an-y boy loves an-y toy. No lit-tle girl cares.

There's the lit-tle se - cret she must keep that she can fly when

she's a - sleep. Ev-'ry lit-tle girl would like to be the

fai - ry on the Christ-mas tree. Christ-mas tree. Oh the

LET IT SNOW! LET IT SNOW! LET IT SNOW!

Words by SAMMY CAHN
Music by JULE STYNE

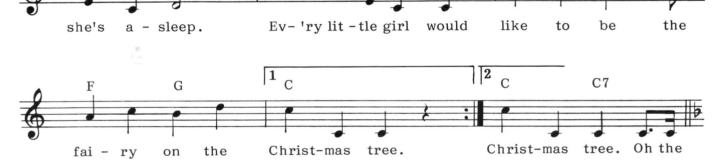

wea-ther out - side is fright-ful But the fire is so de-

light - ful, And since we've no place to go, Let it

THE LITTLE BOY THAT SANTA CLAUS FORGOT

Words and Music by MICHAEL CARR,
TOMMIE CONNOR and JIMMY LEACH

lit - tle boy that San - ta Claus for - got ——— And

good - ness knows, he did - n't want a lot. ——— He

sent a note to San - ta for some sol - diers and a drum, It

broke his lit - tle heart when he found San - ta had - n't come. In the

street he en - vies all those luck - y boys, ——— Then

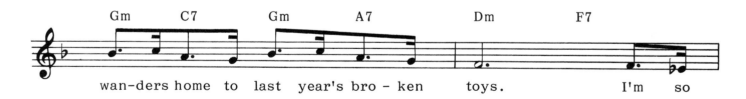

wan - ders home to last year's bro - ken toys. I'm so

sor - ry for that lad - die, he has - n't got a dad - dy, The

lit - tle boy that San - ta Claus for - got. He's the - got.

BB1
116

Medley 5

IT CAME UPON THE MIDNIGHT CLEAR

Traditional

It —

came up - on the — mid - night clear, That glor - ious song — of

old, From — an - gels bend - ing near the earth To —

touch — their harps of gold: "Peace on the earth, good -

- will to men, From heaven's all gra - cious King!" The

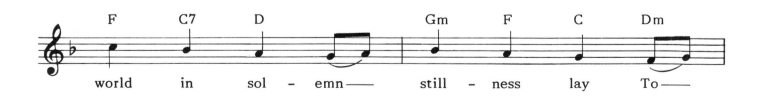

world in sol - emn — still - ness lay To —

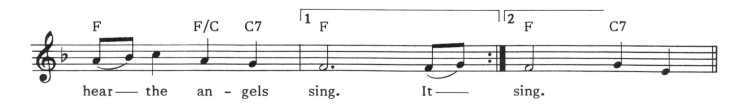

hear — the an - gels sing. It — sing.

LITTLE JESUS, SWEETLY SLEEP

Traditional

Lit - tle Je - sus, sweet - ly— sleep, do not— stir;

We will— lend a— coat of— fur; We will rock you,

rock you, rock you, We will rock you,

rock you, rock you; See the fur to keep you— warm,

Snug - ly— round your— ti - ny— form. ti - ny— form.

SEE, AMID THE WINTER'S SNOW

Traditional

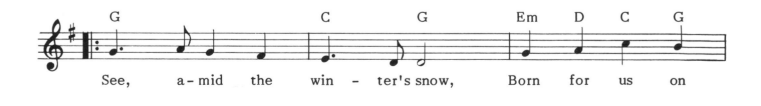

See, a-mid the win - ter's snow, Born for us on

earth be - low, See, the Lamb of God ap-pears,

Prom - ised from e - ter - nal years.

Hail, thou ev - er - bless - èd morn! Hail, re-demp-tion's

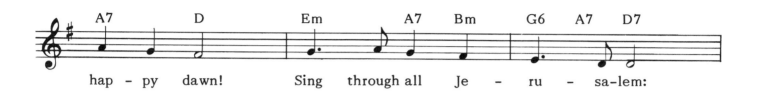

hap - py dawn! Sing through all Je - ru - sa-lem:

Christ is born in Beth - le - hem. Beth - le - hem. While

WHILE SHEPHERDS WATCHED

Traditional

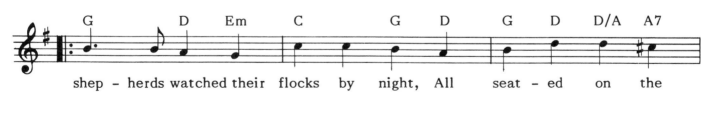

shep - herds watched their flocks by night, All seat - ed on the

ground, The an - gel of the Lord came down, And glo - ry shone a -

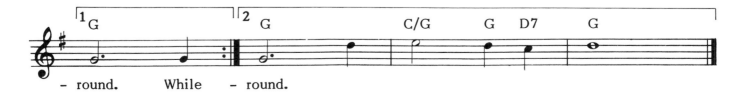

- round. While - round.

Waltz 110

Medley 6

THE FIRST NOWELL

Traditional

The— first — Now - ell the— an - gel did
say Was to cer - tain poor shep-herds in fields as they
lay; In— fields— where— they lay,— keep-ing their
sheep. On a cold win - ter's night — that
was — so deep: Now - ell, — Now -
— ell, Now - ell, Now - ell, Born is the
king — of Is - ra - el. The — el. The

THE HOLLY AND THE IVY

Traditional

hol-ly and the i - vy, When they are both full -

grown, Of — all the trees that are in the wood, The —

hol-ly bears the crown. O the ris-ing of the

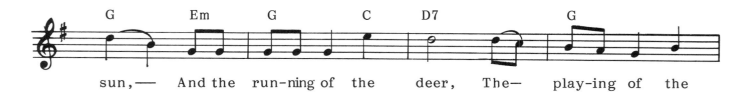

sun,— And the run-ning of the deer, The— play-ing of the

mer-ry or-gan,Sweet sing-ing in the choir. The choir. Ci-ty

SILVER BELLS

Words and Music by JAY LIVINGSTON and RAY EVANS

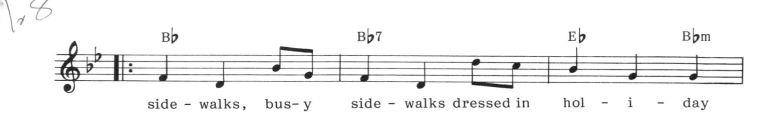

side - walks, bus- y side - walks dressed in hol - i - day

style. In the air there's a feel - ing of

THE COVENTRY CAROL

Traditional

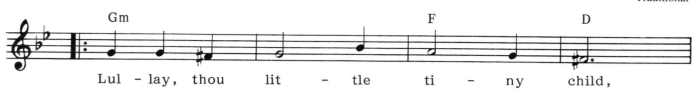

Lul - lay, thou lit - tle ti - ny child,

Bye, bye, lul - ly, lul - lay.————— Lul -

lay, thou lit - tle ti - ny child,

Bye, bye lul - ly, lul - lay.—————

Her - od the king in his rag - ing,

charg - ed he hath this day.————— His

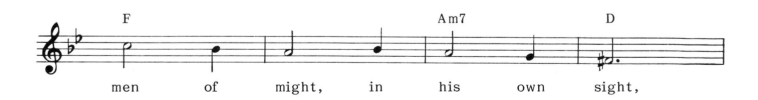

men of might, in his own sight,

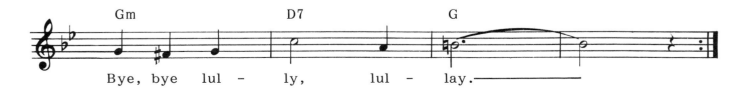

Bye, bye lul - ly, lul - lay.—————

Medley 7

Handwritten notes:
- To Party 100
- Trad 3
- Split F2   Trans D
- 100
- 1 Wide Musette
- 2 Octave Horns
- 3 Slow Strings

JOLLY OLD SAINT NICHOLAS

Traditional

Jol-ly old Saint Nich-o-las Lean your ear this way. Don't you tell a sin-gle soul what I'm going to say, Christ-mas Eve is com-ing soon Now you dear old man. Whis-per what you'll bring to me, tell me if you can. Oh, can. You

SANTA CLAUS IS COMIN' TO TOWN

Words by HAVEN GILLESPIE
Music by J FRED COOTS

bet-ter watch out you bet-ter not cry;
mak-ing a list and checking it twice;

Bet-ter not pout I'm
Gon-na find out who's

tell-ing you why:}
naugh-ty or nice:}

San-ta Claus is com-ing to town. He's town. He

sees you when you're sleep-ing; He knows when you're a - wake. He

knows if you've been bad or good, so be good for good-ness sake. You

bet-ter watch out you bet-ter not cry; bet-ter not pout I'm tell-ing you why:

1

San - ta Claus is com-ing to town. ———— He

2

com - ing to town. ———— Just hear those

SLEIGH RIDE

Words by MITCHELL PARISH
Music by LEROY ANDERSON

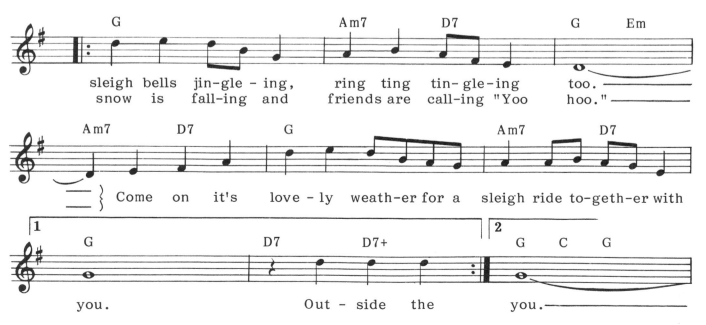

sleigh bells jin-gle - ing, ring ting tin-gle-ing too. ————
snow is fall-ing and friends are call-ing "Yoo hoo." ————

Come on it's love - ly weath-er for a sleigh ride to-geth-er with

1

2

you. Out - side the you. ————

RUDOLPH THE RED-NOSED REINDEER

Words and Music by JOHNNY MARKS

Medley 8

AS WITH GLADNESS MEN OF OLD

Traditional

men of old   Did the guid - ing   star be - hold,

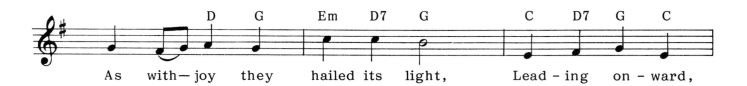

As with — joy they hailed its light,   Lead - ing on - ward,

beam - ing bright.   So, most grac - ious   God, may we

Ev - er - more be led to thee.   led to thee.

DECK THE HALLS

Traditional

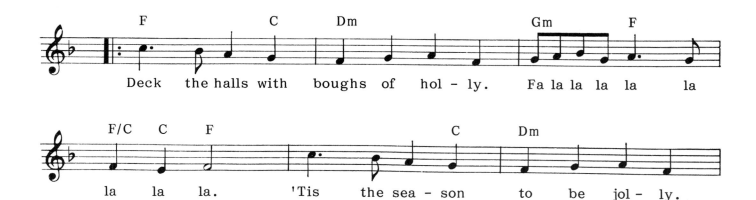

Deck the halls with boughs of hol - ly.   Fa la la la la   la

la la la.   'Tis the sea - son   to be jol - ly.

Fa la la la la la la la la. Don we now our

gay ap-pa-rel. Fa la la la la la la la la.

Troll the an-cient Yule-tide car-ol. Fa la la la la la

la la la. la la la. Oh when the

I WISH IT COULD BE CHRISTMAS EVERY DAY

Words and Music by ROY WOOD

snow-man brings the snow, — oh well he

just might like to know — He's put a great big smile

on some-bod-y's face. ——— If you

CHRISTMAS ALPHABET

Words and Music by BUDDY KAYE and JULES LOMAN

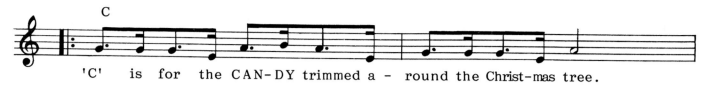

'C' is for the CAN-DY trimmed a - round the Christ-mas tree.

'H' is for the HAP-PI-NESS with all the fam-i-ly.

'R' is for the REIN-DEER pranc-ing by the win - dow pane.

'I' is for the IC - ING on the cake as sweet as su-gar cane.

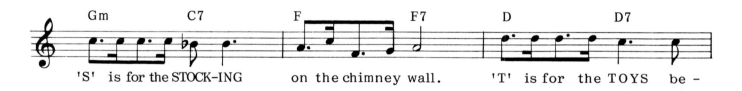

'S' is for the STOCK-ING on the chimney wall. 'T' is for the TOYS be -

neath the tree so tall. 'M' is for the MIS-TLETOE where ev-ery-one is kissed.

'A' is for the ANGELS who make up the Christmas list. 'S' is for old SANTA who makes

ev - ery kid his pet. Be good and he'll bring you ev-ery-thing in your

1.
CHRIST-MAS AL - PHA-BET.

2.
CHRIST-MAS AL - PHA-BET.

Medley 9

GOOD CHRISTIAN MEN REJOICE

Traditional

March 1
80

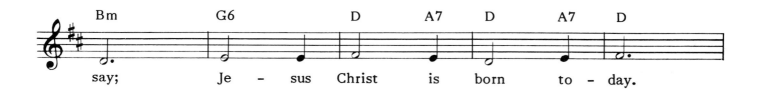

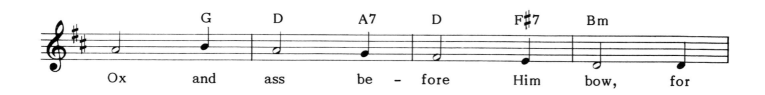

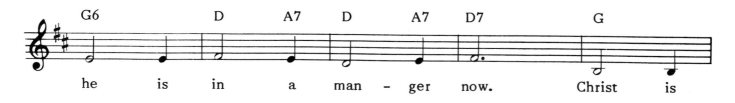

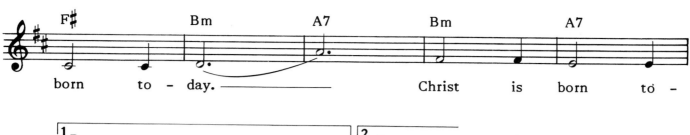

born to - day. ———————— Christ is born to -

- day. ———————— Good - day.

WE THREE KINGS

Traditional

We three kings of O - rient are;

Bear - ing gifts we tra - verse a - far. Field and

foun - tain, moor and moun - tain, Fol - low - ing

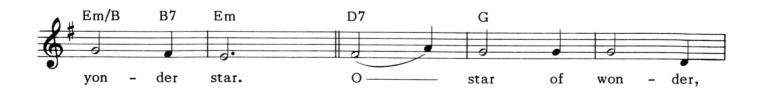

yon - der star. O ——— star of won - der,

star of night, Star with roy - al beau - ty

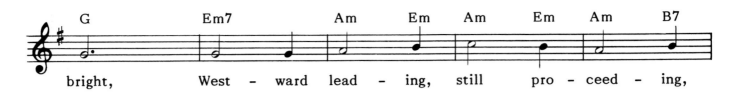

bright,   West - ward lead - ing,   still   pro - ceed - ing,

Guide   us   to   thy   per - fect   light.   light.   I

16 Beat   G3

I SAW THREE SHIPS

Traditional

saw   three   ships   come   sail - ing   in,   On   Christ - mas

day,   on   Christ - mas   day;   I   saw   three   ships   come

sail - ing   in,   On   Christ - mas   day   in   the   morn -

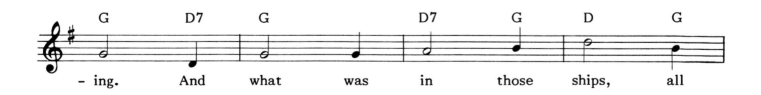

- ing.   And   what   was   in   those   ships,   all

three,   On   Christ - mas   day,   on   Christ - mas

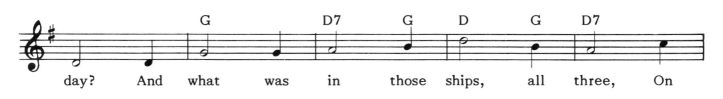

day? And what was in those ships, all three, On

Christ - mas day in the morn - ing?

16 Beat 1
93

HERE WE COME A-WASSAILING

Traditional

♩. = ♩. (L'estesso tempo)

Here we come a - was - sail-ing A - mong the leaves so green.

Here we come a - wan - der-ing so fair — to be seen. Love and

joy come to you and to you your was - sail too, and God

bless you and send — you a Hap - py New Year. And God send you a

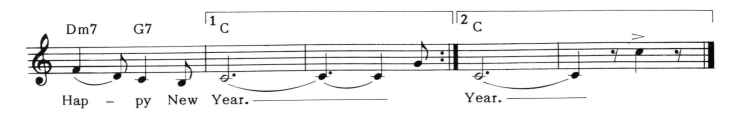

Hap - py New Year. ——— Year. ———

Medley 10

Trad 3
80+

DING DONG MERRILY ON HIGH

Traditional

Ding dong mer-ri-ly on

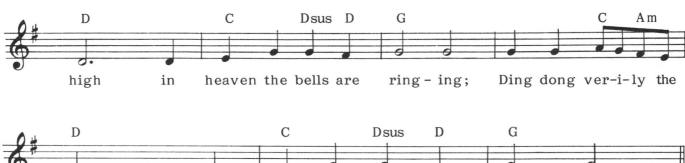

high   in heaven the bells are ring - ing;   Ding dong ver-i-ly the

sky   is   riv'n with an - gel sing - ing.

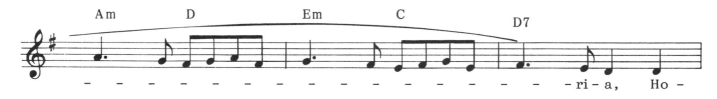

Glo - - - - - - - - - - - - - - - - -

- - - - - - - - - - - - - - - -ri-a,   Ho -

san - na in ex - cel - sis.   cel - sis.

LITTLE DRUMMER BOY

Words and Music by HARRY SIMEONE,
HENRY ONORATI and KATHERINE K DAVIS

Come   they told   me, pa - rum pum pum pum,

A new born King to see, pa - rum pum pum pum, —

Our fin - est gifts we bring, pa - rum pum pum pum, —

To lay be - fore the King, pa - rum pum pum pum,

rum pum pum pum, rum pum pum pum, — — So to

hon - our Him, pa - rum pum pum pum, —

When— we come. —

FROSTY THE SNOWMAN

Words and Music by STEVE NELSON and JACK ROLLINS

Frost - y the snow-man was a jol - ly hap - py soul—

— With a corn cob pipe and a but-ton nose— and two

JINGLE BELLS

Traditional

Medley 11

ONCE IN ROYAL DAVID'S CITY

Traditional

Once in roy - al

Dav - id's— ci - ty   Stood a   low - ly   cat - tle— shed,

Where a   Moth - er   laid— her— Ba - by   In a   man - ger

for— His— bed.   Ma - ry   was   that   Moth - er   mild,

Je - sus   Christ   Her   lit - tle— Child.   lit - tle— Child.

LITTLE DONKEY

Words and Music by ERIC BOSWELL

Lit - tle don - key, lit - tle don - key, on the dust - y   road.

Got to keep   on   plod - ding on - wards with your pre - cious   load.

WINTER WONDERLAND

Words by DICK SMITH
Music by FELIX BERNARD

Francis, Day & Hunter Ltd., London WC2H 0EA/Redwood Music Ltd., London NW1 8BD

fi – re   To face un-a-fraid— the   plans that we made,—

Walk-ing   in   a   win-ter   won-der-land.   Sleigh bells   -land.

HARK! THE HERALD ANGELS SING

Traditional

Hark! the her – ald   an-gels sing—   Glo -ry   to   the   new-born King,

Peace   on   earth,   and   mer – cy   mild,—   God   and   sin – ners

re – con – ciled.   Joy – ful   all   ye   na – tions, rise,—

Join   the   tri – umph   of   the   skies; —   With   th'an-gel – ic

host   pro – claim,   Christ is— born   in   Beth – le – hem.

Hark! the her-ald   an-gels sing   Glo-ry— to   the   new-born King.

Medley 12

AWAY IN A MANGER

Traditional

Waltz
115.

A - way in a —

man - ger, no — crib for a bed, the —

lit - tle Lord Je - sus lay — down his sweet

head. The stars in the— bright sky look— down where he

lay; the— lit - tle Lord Je - sus a —

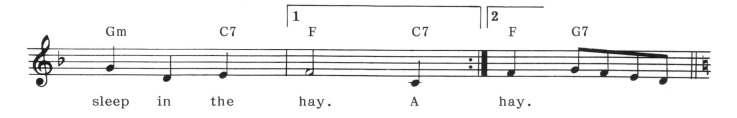

sleep in the man - ger, in the hay. A hay.

CHILD IN A MANGER

Traditional

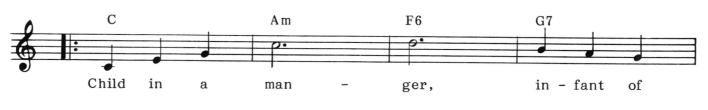

Child in a man - ger, in - fant of

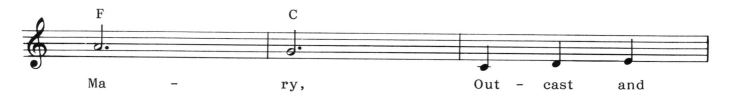

Ma - ry, Out - cast and

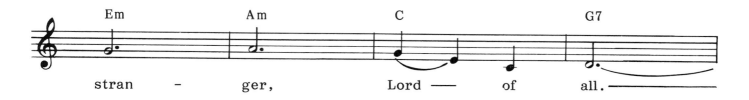

stran - ger, Lord — of all. —

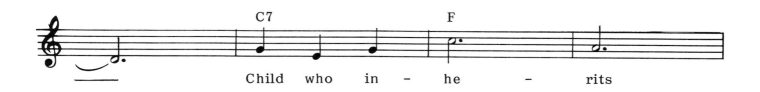

— Child who in - he - rits

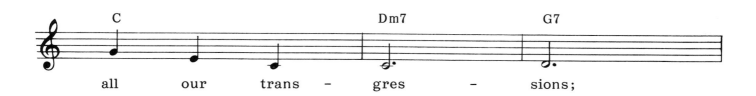

all our trans - gres - sions;

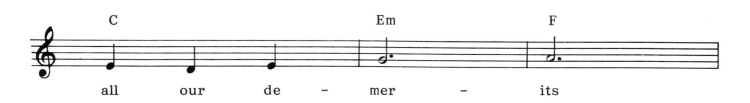

all our de - mer - its

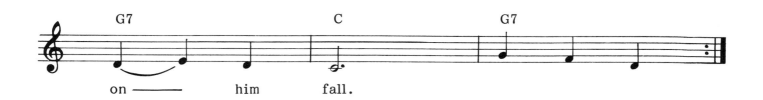

on — him fall.

Wor - thy our Sa - viour of all our

prais - es; Hap - py for ev -

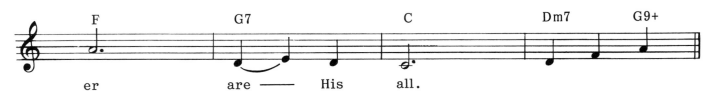

er are —— His all.

SILENT NIGHT

Traditional

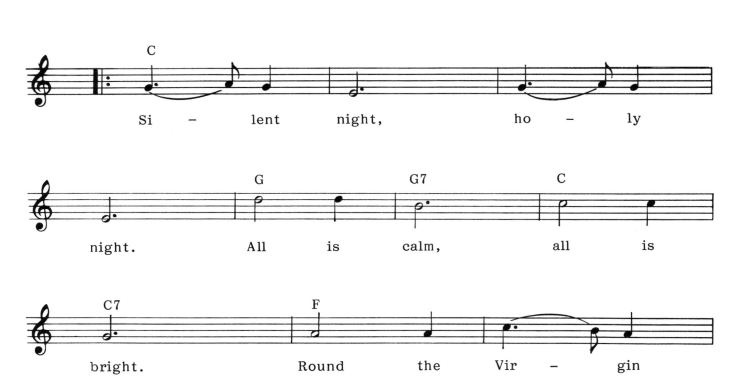

Si - lent night, ho - ly

night. All is calm, all is

bright. Round the Vir - gin

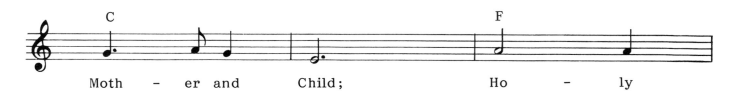

Moth - er and Child; Ho - ly

In - fant so ten - der and mild.

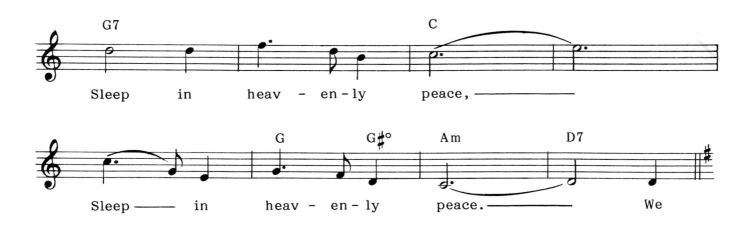

Sleep in heav - en - ly peace, ———

Sleep ——— in heav - en - ly peace. ——— We

WE WISH YOU A MERRY CHRISTMAS

Traditional

wish you a mer-ry Christ-mas, We wish you a mer-ry

Christ - mas, We wish you a mer-ry Christ-mas and a

hap - py new year. Glad ti - dings we bring to

you and your kin. We wish you a mer-ry

Christ - mas and a hap - py new year. We

year, a hap - py new year.

Medley 13

THE CHRISTMAS SONG (CHESTNUTS ROASTING ON AN OPEN FIRE)

Words and Music by MEL TORME
and ROBERT WELLS

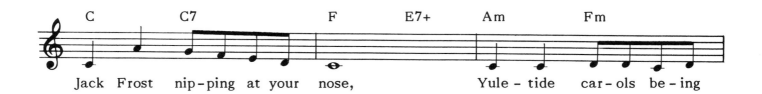

Chest-nuts roast-ing on an o-pen fire,

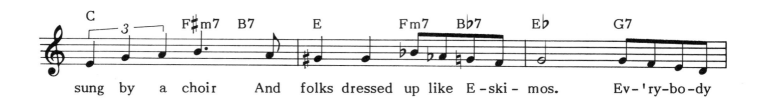

Jack Frost nip-ping at your nose, Yule-tide car-ols be-ing

sung by a choir And folks dressed up like E-ski-mos. Ev-'ry-bo-dy

knows a turkey and some mistle-toe Help to make the season bright.

Ti-ny tots with their eyes all a-glow Will find it hard to sleep to-

-night. They know that San-ta's on his way;—— He's load-ed

lots of toys and goodies on his sleigh And ev-'ry moth-er's child—— is gon-na

spy ——— To see if rein-deer—real-ly know how to fly. ——— And

so, I'm of-fer-ing this sim - ple phrase To kids from one to nine-ty -

- two. Al-though it's been said ma-ny times, ma-ny ways; "Mer-ry

Christ - mas to you."   you."   A ray of

WHEN A CHILD IS BORN

Words by FRED JAY
Music by ZACAR

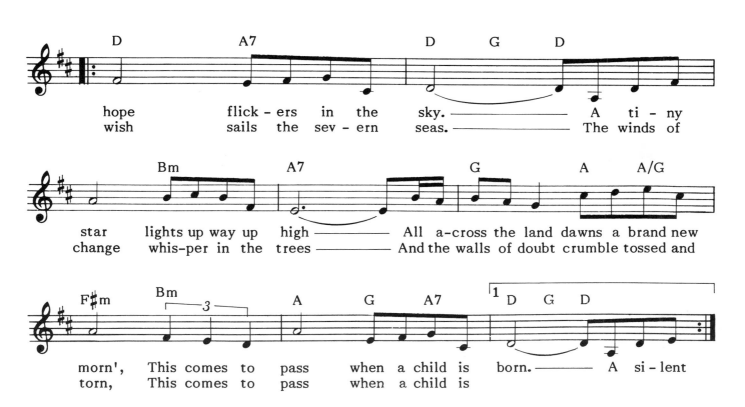

hope   flick - ers in the   sky. ——————— A ti - ny
wish   sails the sev - ern seas. ——————— The winds of

star   lights up way up high ——— All a-cross the land dawns a brand new
change whis-per in the trees ——— And the walls of doubt crumble tossed and

morn', This comes to pass when a child is born.——— A si - lent
torn, This comes to pass when a child is

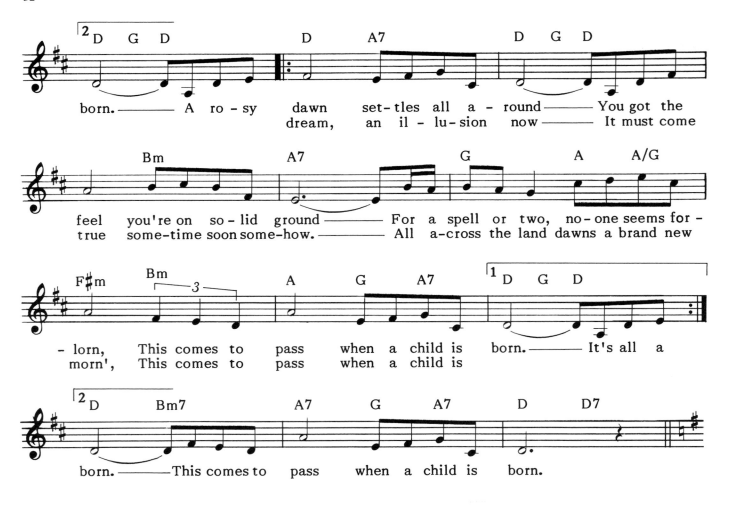

MARY'S BOY CHILD

Words and Music by JESTER HAIRSTON

54

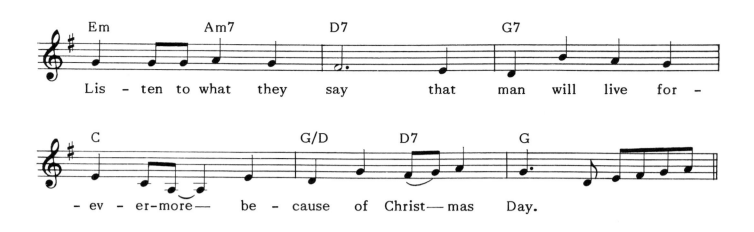

ANGELS FROM THE REALMS OF GLORY

Traditional

Trad 2
140

Medley 14

I SAW MOMMY KISSING SANTA CLAUS

Show ballad 130
1) Seaside Organ
2) Tibia Chorus   Split F 2
3) Theatre Org

Words and Music by TOMMIE CONNOR

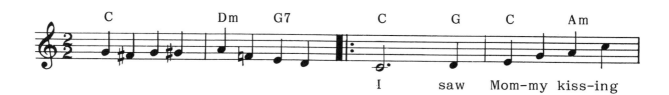

I saw Mom-my kiss-ing

San - ta Claus   Un-der-neath the mis-tle-toe last

night; ——— She did-n't see me creep down the

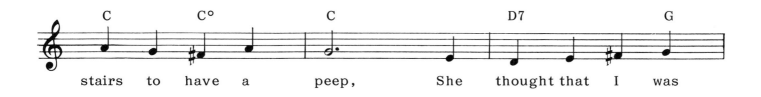

stairs to have a peep, She thought that I was

tucked up in my bed-room fast a - sleep. Then

I saw Mom-my tick-le San - ta Claus

Un-der-neath his beard so snow-y white; ———

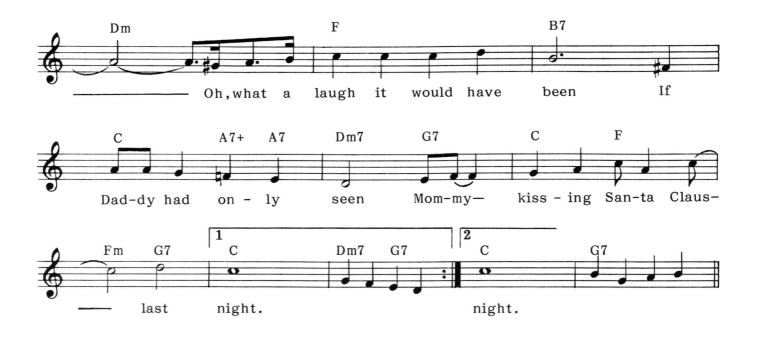

Oh, what a laugh it would have been If Dad-dy had on-ly seen Mom-my— kiss-ing San-ta Claus— —last night. night.

JOY TO THE WORLD

Traditional

Joy to the world; the Lord has come. Let earth re-ceive her king.— Let e-v'ry— heart— pre-pare— Him— room.— And heaven and na-ture— sing, And— heaven and na-ture— sing, And— heav-en and heav-en and na-ture sing. sing. Mis-ter

MISTER SANTA (MISTER SANDMAN)

Words and Music by PAT BALLARD

MERRY CHRISTMAS EVERYONE

Words and Music by BOB HEATLIE

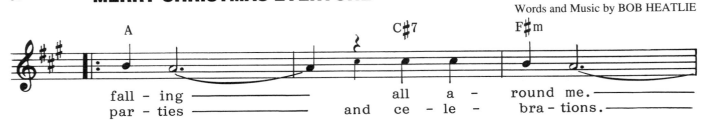

fall - ing _____ all a - round me._____
par - ties _____ and ce - le - bra - tions._____

_____ Child - ren play - ing; _____ hav - ing
_____ Peo - ple dan - cing _____ all night

fun. _____ It's the sea - son _____ of
long. _____ Time for pre - sents, _____

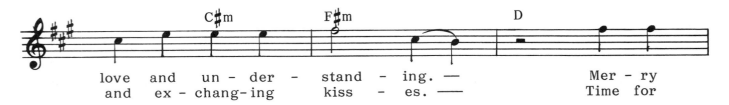

love and un - der - stand - ing. — Mer - ry
and ex - chang - ing kiss - es. — Time for

1

Christ - mas _____ Eve - ry - one._____ Time for
sing - ing _____ Christ-mas

2

songs. _____ We're gon - na

have a par - ty to - night. _____

I'm gon - na find that girl; un - der-neath—the

Medley 15

O LITTLE TOWN OF BETHLEHEM

Traditional

O lit – tle town of Beth – le – hem, How still we—see thee lie. A – bove thy deep and dream—less—sleep The si – lent—stars go by. Yet— in the dark—streets— shin – eth The ev – er – last – ing light; The hopes and fears of all—the—years Are met in—thee to – night. O – night.

IN THE BLEAK MID-WINTER

Traditional

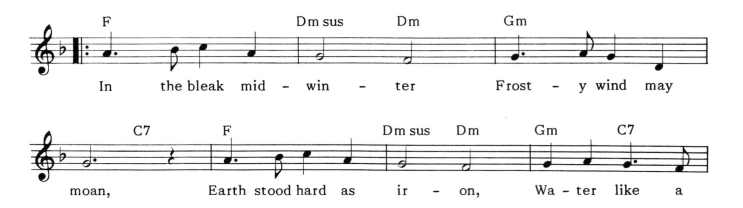

In the bleak mid – win – ter Frost – y wind may moan, Earth stood hard as ir – on, Wa – ter like a

stone; Snow had fall - en, snow on snow,

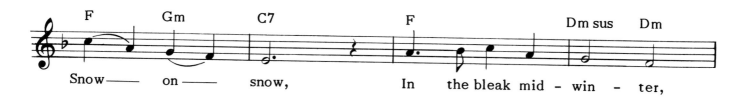

Snow — on — snow, In the bleak mid - win - ter,

Long — a - go. - go. — A

A CHILD THIS DAY IS BORN

Traditional

Child this day is — born, A Child of high — re -

- nown, Most wor - thy of — a scep - tre, A

scep - tre and a crown. Now - ell, Now - ell, Now —

- ell, Now - ell, sing all — we may, Be -

©1992 International Music Publications Southend Road, Woodford Green, Essex IG8 8HN

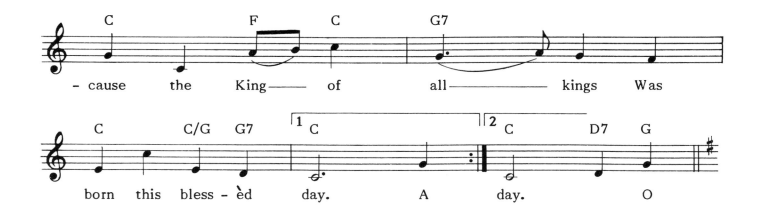

O COME ALL YE FAITHFUL

Traditional

Printed in England
The Panda Group · Haverhill · Suffolk · 10/96